READING 2000 ✦ LEVEL FOU

CW00431886

n.6

The Story of Shaheen

Helen Murdoch

Oliver & Boyd

Acknowledgements

Illustrated by Cheryl Tarbuck

Oliver & Boyd
Longman House
Burnt Mill, Harlow
Essex CM20 2JE

An Imprint of Longman Group UK Ltd

© Oliver & Boyd Ltd 1991

First published 1991

ISBN 0 05 0050370

Set in Plantin 12 on 18pt
Printed in Hong Kong
Produced by Longman Group (F.E.) Ltd.

The Story of
Shaheen

A play loosely adapted from elements in Indian and Pakistani folk tales

---

Characters

Akbar, a rich merchant

Razia, his wife

Sophia ⎫
Zara ⎪
Rayesa ⎪
Zarreen ⎬ their seven daughters
Mahreen ⎪
Nadia ⎪
Shaheen ⎭

Sabeen, their old nurse

First Storyteller

Second Storyteller

Third Storyteller

First Servant

Second Servant

Third Servant

Fourth Servant

Prince Omar Sabar

Prince Anjum ⎫
Prince Faraz ⎪
Prince Zaki ⎬ his six brothers
Prince Haroun ⎪
Prince Nabil ⎪
Prince Saad ⎭

Court Magician

Mr and Mrs Magic Bird

Ahmed, servant to Akbar

Overseer

First Townsman

Second Townsman

First Townswoman

Second Townswoman

The Sheltering Tree

Also Tigers, Peacocks, Stallholders, Prince's retinue, Workers.

Time: Once upon a time

Place: A faraway country in the east

Act 1, Scene 1

*The garden of Akbar, a rich merchant. He sits with his wife
Razia, upstage left, with their daughters beside them. Sophia,
Zara, Rayesa, Zarreen, Mahreen and Nadia are doing nothing
except look elegant, but Shaheen, the youngest, is reading. They
all remain perfectly still, like a picture, as the Three Storytellers
enter and bow to the audience. The First Storyteller steps forward.*

First Storyteller: This is the lovely garden of a rich
merchant, Akbar. There he is, sitting beside his wife and
seven daughters, the very picture of happiness.

*First Storyteller moves downstage right, and sits down,
cross-legged.*

Second Storyteller (*stepping forward*): Akbar has many ships that sail the seven seas, trading in silks, spices and precious stones. So successful is he that the whole family live a life of luxury, as happy as riches and possessions can make them.

Second Storyteller goes to sit alongside the First.

Third Storyteller (*stepping forward*): Indeed, six of his daughters thought that they were happy because they were rich – and not rich because they were happy, which was something they had yet to learn about. They thought fine clothes and jewels were the most important things in life.

Third Storyteller goes to sit beside the other two.

First Storyteller: Their father loved to give them new dresses and jewellery, and so they vied with each other for his affection – and the gifts he lavished upon them.

Second Storyteller: But what about the seventh daughter?

Third Storyteller: The seventh daughter is Shaheen. And she is different from her older sisters.

Second Storyteller: Look at her now! She's reading a book.

First Storyteller: But her sisters – they're looking after their father – or so it would seem.

The three storytellers now become silent and remain still, as Akbar, Razia and their seven daughters come to life.

Sophia: Father, you look hot. Let me fetch you a cool drink.

Exit Sophia. Zara crosses to her father.

Zara: Father, you seem worried. Shall I ask the musicians to play for you?

Akbar: No, my dear. I would rather listen to the music of your words.

Sophia enters with a goblet.

Akbar: Thank you, Sophia. How well you look after your old father.

Rayesa: Not 'old', Father! Never 'old'!

Razia: Silly girls! Don't fuss so much!

Akbar: They fuss, as you call it, to show their affection. Clearly I am the very source of their happiness. Is it not so, my daughters?

Six Daughters (*all together*): Absolutely so, beloved Father!

Akbar: You see, my dear. Such love they have for me.

Razia: That's as may be.

Akbar: Do you doubt their affection for me?

Razia: Is there reason to doubt it, do you think?

Akbar (*annoyed*): I can see you need some proof. I will put them to the test. My daughters, stand before me. Come, Shaheen, put aside your book.

Razia: What were you reading, Shaheen?

Shaheen: A wonderful book about herbs and wild flowers. It has cures for all sorts of complaints – rheumatism, indigestion, the common cold...

Sophia: She'll be off gathering herbs by the river...

Zara: She'll be brewing up some awful concoction in the kitchen next...

Nadia: It'll smell the whole house out...

Shaheen: The salve I made last week cured your spots, Rayesa.

Rayesa: They were getting better anyway.

Shaheen: And the herbal tea cured your cold, Zarreen.

Zarreen: Yes, I suppose so. But it didn't taste very nice.

Akbar: In the market, in the kitchen, brewing up remedies like some gypsy – that's no way to behave!

Razia: It's more useful than sitting in the sun all day long.

Zara: That's not fair, Mother!

Rayesa: You always favour Shaheen.

Razia: Your father spoils you all. You are indolent and selfish. What do you ever do for other people? How could you cope in the real world – if you had to work?

The girls look indignant, and shrug their shoulders.

Sophia: But we don't have to work, Mother.

Razia: Lucky for you, you don't!

Akbar: Come, my dear, you are too hard on them. They are dutiful daughters to their old father. . . and their mother, of course. Girls! Let me ask you a question. On whom does your well-being depend?

Sophia: As the eldest, I will speak first. As the fields of grain depend upon the warmth of the mighty sun to turn them to gleaming gold, so does my well-being depend upon your generosity, my Father.

Akbar: Well said, Sophia. See how my children love me! This proves their affection for me.

Razia: Yes – if words were deeds.

Akbar: And what has our youngest to say? Shaheen, speak now.

Shaheen: Father, I love you and my mother as a daughter should. But as for my life, I must learn to stand on my own two feet and depend on no-one but myself.

Akbar: What? Can a child of mine be so ungrateful, so selfish?

Shaheen: Not selfish, Father, but self-reliant.

Akbar: Don't speak to me like that! So this is how you feel! Then you shall go empty-handed into the world and then see how you can get on without your father's help! Begone with you, before the sun sets!

Akbar turns upstage, his back to Shaheen.

Razia: Akbar, you are too hasty.

Akbar: Shaheen has spoken her mind, and so have I.

Nadia: But Father, I don't think Shaheen meant to upset you.

Akbar: Be off with you, all of you, unless you wish to be banished with your ungrateful sister.

All exeunt except Shaheen.

Shaheen: How harsh my father's words are! Yet I love him, for all his anger. But I feel certain I am right. The only way to face up to life is to stand on my own two feet.

Re-enter Razia, with a bundle tied neatly.

Razia: My poor daughter! You spoke truly, but your father's anger clouds his vision. Now you must travel the world. Meet life bravely. Do not forget us.

Shaheen: I'll never forget you, or my father, or my sisters.

Enter Sabeen, the old nurse who had looked after the girls when they were little.

Sabeen: What's this I hear? Our baby to be cast out of her own home? What harm has she ever done?

Shaheen: Alas, Sabeen, my plain words sounded harsh. And so my own father has banished me.

Sabeen: You will not go alone, for I am coming with you. I can still look after a house, and cook and clean.

Shaheen: Dear Nurse, there will be no house to look after, only the sky above. And there will be little to cook, for there will be scant money for food.

Sabeen: All the better! There will be less work for me. Come along, girl. We'll meet our adventures together.

Razia: It is time for you to go. Look – the sun is nearly setting. Let me say goodbye now, for I cannot bear to see you vanish into the night.

Shaheen: Don't worry, Mother! When I have made my way in the world, I'll come back to you. Take good care of yourself, and of my father. Come, Sabeen, let's get ready.

(End of Scene 1.)

Act 1, Scene 2

Far in the country. The Sheltering Tree is upstage right. Shaheen and Sabeen are having a look around.

Shaheen: What strange wild place is this? But here we must rest for we can go no further.

Sabeen (*jumping*): What's that?

Shaheen: Just a bird – I think.

Sabeen: A bird I can cope with.

The roaring of a tiger is heard.

Sabeen: That's not a bird!

Shaheen: No. We'd better find a safer place to sleep.

Sabeen: Quick, Shaheen – climb that tree!

Shaheen: No, you go first.

Sabeen: I'm too old to climb trees.

Shaheen: Try to climb! Please try! The tiger is coming!

Enter Mr and Mrs Bird.

Mr Bird: Don't despair.

Shaheen: Oh! Who are you?

Mrs Bird: He's one, and I'm one too.

Mr Bird: We're two magical birds. We're here to help
people . . . people who deserve help. I think you do.

Mrs Bird: I think so too.

Shaheen: Please help us! The tiger's coming.

Mr Bird: Don't you see – the tree?

Mrs Bird: The tree will shelter you. Look at him. He'll
spread his branches to make a shield for you.

Tree: What's this? It's a bit late. I'm closed for the night.

Shaheen: Oh, please, Mr Tree. Sabeen and I will be eaten by the tiger if you don't help.

Tree: That pesky tiger again, is it? Anything to spoil his wicked plans. Stand back. Here goes.

The tree spreads its branches out like great arms, and Shaheen and Sabeen step inside.

Tree: There you are. Go to sleep and forget about the tiger.

Mr Bird: A nice girl. I think we'll help her.

Mrs Bird: A good idea. But the tree will keep them safe until tomorrow.

Mr and Mrs Bird go off. The tiger enters, then another. Although they sniff around, they do not find Shaheen and Sabeen.

(End of Scene 2.)

Act 1, Scene 3

Morning. Sabeen sits under the tree. Shaheen enters with a basket.

Shaheen: What a lovely day! And look – wild plums for lunch.

Sabeen: A lovely day! Our sleep disturbed by tigers, and nothing to eat but the fruits of the wilderness!

Shaheen: It could be worse. Our friend the tree has saved us. How nice it is to sleep outside, when we know we are safe.

Sabeen: Still, it's a hard life for a young girl to have to make her own way in the world.

Shaheen: I believe in standing on my own two feet.

The two magic birds fly in.

Shaheen: There you are. Do you really talk?

Mr Bird: Yes, here we are. And we talk. What can we do . . .

Mrs Bird: . . . for you?

Shaheen: I wouldn't mind your advice about earning a living in this strange world.

Mr Bird: Nothing easier. Anything else?

Sabeen (*in a whisper*): Ask how we can eat every day!

Mrs Bird: Your friend is practical. Both your wishes will be granted – in this way. Take what money you have, and go to the market in the village down by the river. Buy some boiled rice, as much as you can get and bring it here.

Shaheen: Here is all the money I have. Will it be enough?

Sabeen: Give it to me. I'll get a better bargain than you, for all your clever ways.

Shaheen: What would I do without you?

Sabeen: I often wonder!

Exit Sabeen.

Mr Bird: Now, do exactly as we say. But rest awhile under the magic tree again, and we'll send you a special dream.

Shaheen: I feel sleepy. I will lie down, just for a little while.

She spreads out her shawl and lies down to sleep.

Mrs Bird (*softly*): A good girl... A kind girl.

Mr Bird: Who will work hard not for herself but to help others.

Mr Bird ⎫
Mrs Bird ⎭ : Sleep in the shade of the magical tree,
Sleep while we plan what your future will be.
Bright days are coming, the dull times are past.
The sorrowful moments are over at last.

Exeunt Mr and Mrs Bird. There's a short musical interlude. The Three Storytellers enter.

First Storyteller: And so Shaheen can rest, knowing that her friends the birds are looking after her.

Second Storyteller: It is a wonderful thing to have friends.

Third Storyteller: Even if they are only feathered friends.

First Storyteller (*shocked*):   All friends are wonderful.

First Storyteller: Shaheen is now in their care.

After a short pause, Shaheen awakes.

Shaheen: What a marvellous dream!
I saw a wonderful house, and my
mother and father and sisters were
all there with me. We were so happy.
Then there came a handsome Prince.
He was looking for someone. But
when I asked him if I could help, he
only smiled and bowed and said '*Sabar*'!
Sabar, in this country, means 'Be patient'!
What can it all mean?

Mr Bird: It seems to be a happy dream,
so wait and see.

*Re-enter Sabeen, carrying a large
bowl of rice.*

Sabeen: Look at my bargain. The first stall-holder laughed at the small amount of money I offered. The second man was too busy to serve me. But the third wanted to shut up shop and go home, so he sold me all this rice, ready to eat. And now, let's sit down and eat, for I'm hungry.

Shaheen: Will you share our supper, Mrs Bird?

Mrs Bird: No, thank you, Shaheen. Take only as much rice as you need for your supper, and no more. Then divide the rest into three bowls. Before you go to sleep tonight, place each bowl at three points around the tree.

(Exeunt Mr and Mrs Bird.)

Sabeen: Seems like a waste of good food to me!

Shaheen: Nevertheless, Sabeen, we will do what our wise friends tell us.

Shaheen and Sabeen put the rice in the bowls. The lights dim and Shaheen and Sabeen go to sleep. Music plays. A peacock enters, examines the bowls of rice, then beckons to the other peacocks offstage. The other peacocks enter warily, and then, as they crowd around the rice bowls, their tail feathers get ruffled and drop off.

Third Storyteller: Look! The ground is almost covered with their feathers.

First Storyteller: The peacocks will soon grow more. These are for Shaheen.

Second Storyteller: What use are they to Shaheen?

First Storyteller: Wait and see.

As the music ends, the peacocks leave the stage. The light comes up to represent daybreak. Shaheen wakes up.

Shaheen: Oh, it's morning already! But everything looks different! The ground has become a sea, a sea of blue and green feathers!

She picks up some feathers and holds them in the shape of a fan. She parades up and down, fanning herself.

Shaheen: Look, Sabeen! Are you awake yet?

Sabeen: Who could sleep with you babbling on about feathers? And where did you get that beautiful fan?

Shaheen: The peacocks have eaten the rice. They left these – for us, I suppose.

Sabeen: Many a fine lady would love to buy a fan like that.

Shaheen: You're right! If I made fans, we could sell them!

Sabeen: I think you've hit on a good idea!

Shaheen and Sabeen go off, their arms full of feathers.

(End of Scene 3.)

Act 1, Scene 4

Several months later. Shaheen's stall, with a display of peacock fans, is downstage right. Sabeen is arranging them. A white doorway, upstage left, represents the grand house that is being built for Shaheen, who has become rich selling her fans.

Sabeen: At last you've come. The fans are selling as fast as you can make them.

Shaheen: Don't worry. There were even more peacocks – and tail feathers – last night. We must put out extra rice.

Sabeen: You've done well in less than a year.

Shaheen: Only because you helped me. When the new house is built, you'll sleep in a feather bed!

Sabeen: Four walls and a roof will be welcome before the cold nights come.

Shaheen: Everything is working out as I had hoped, thanks to the Magic Birds. I am the happiest girl in the world – except...

Sabeen: Yes?

Shaheen: I can't help thinking of my mother and father. I would like to see them again.

Sabeen: Your father caused you much unhappiness.

Shaheen: What unhappiness? He sent me away and look what I've learned. I've found work, I've become rich.

Sabeen: He sent you away with harsh words.

Shaheen: That was because of his love for me. And I want to see him again, so that he knows I still love him. If I make the journey, will you look after the stall?

Sabeen: Of course. But will you be safe – travelling such a long way alone?

Enter Mr and Mrs Bird.

Mrs Bird: A journey, is it? A long trek home? Why not fly?

Shaheen: Fly?

Mrs Bird: She's a slight little, light little thing.

Mr Bird: She'll do. We'll all take flight together.

The Birds link wings, taking Shaheen between them. All three run lightly round the stage, then "take off" into the wings. Sabeen looks up to wave goodbye.

Act 2, Scene 1

One hour later. Shaheen's stall, as before. Sabeen is seated on a rug, sleeping beside the stall. Enter the Three Storytellers.

Second Storyteller: I wonder where Shaheen is now?

First Storyteller: She is nearer her parents than she thinks.

Third Storyteller: Look, here are more people to work on the new house. I'm sure I've seen them before.

> *Enter the overseer, carrying a whip, followed by shabbily-dressed workers. Among them are Akbar, Razia, and Shaheen's sisters.*

Overseer: You lot go to the west wall and finish the stairs and windows. You two old ones wait here. Tidy up the garden path and pave it with coloured stones before the rich lady owner returns. Hurry now.

> *All exeunt except Akbar and Razia, who begin sweeping the path.*

First Storyteller: Look at Shaheen's family now. Akbar had a run of bad fortune. His ships were lost at sea. Now he and Razia have to work in the fields.

Second Storyteller: What about the selfish daughters?

First Storyteller: Their bad fortune taught them caring and compassion. Look!

Sophia and Zarreen enter, carrying water and food.

Sophia: Sit down, Mother. Rest for a while.

Zarreen: Father, you too. Eat and drink a little before you work any more under the hot sun.

Enter Overseer.

Overseer: What's all this? I didn't employ you to have a picnic. Get to work, or you'll feel the lash of my whip.

He cracks his whip. Sophia and Zarreen run off in terror. Sabeen awakes.

Sabeen: What's all this? Who are you, you great bully?

Overseer: Silence, old woman, or I'll whip you too!

Enter Shaheen and Mr and Mrs Bird.

Shaheen: Thank you, my friends. But surely we've come back to where we started?

Mr Bird: Look before you speak, Shaheen.

Shaheen: Put away that whip! I hired you to build my house, not to enslave others! I'll have you arrested!

Overseer: Mercy, Lady Shaheen. Spare a poor man. I was only trying to get everything finished before you came back. I meant no harm.

Sabeen: Don't listen to him. He's a cruel rascal!

Shaheen: Then he can continue his work. But not as Overseer. You will do the hardest work there is. Your place will be taken by one of those you persecuted.

Exit Overseer, downcast. Shaheen turns to her father, whom she doesn't at first recognise.

Shaheen: You sir! You seem to have an air of authority. Will you organise this squad of workmen for me?

Akbar: For you, I would do anything, to make up for the day I drove you from our home.

Shaheen: Father!

Sabeen: It's the master! And your mother! And look, your sisters are here too!

Enter Shaheen's sisters.

Shaheen: This is the happiest day of my life. Father, I see your fortunes have grown less. Is it not a great mercy that I have prospered in my new life? I have a business,

making and selling fans. I need help with the stall. I need
nimble fingers to make more fans. I have a new house
that needs to be filled with the people I love most in the
world. What do you say?

Akbar: Daughter, your troubles are over! We will all help.

Razia: And I will keep all of them in order.

Mrs Bird: Home, sweet home, no need to roam.

Mr Bird: Happy together, in summer-blue weather.

*Music plays, as the family and Mr and Mrs Bird go
through the doorway to Shaheen's house. The storytellers
stand to watch them go.*

Third Storyteller: But what about the dream? Shaheen had
a wonderful dream, remember?

First Storyteller: Of course, I remember. That is the last,
splendid chapter of Shaheen's story. You will hear about
that presently.

The storytellers bow to the audience.

(End of Scene 1.)

Act 2, Scene 2

Some weeks later. Shaheen is sitting reading outside her house.
Small jars of dried herbs and bunches of fresh leaves, a mortar and
pestle, lie on the table beside her. Enter Akbar, now richly dressed.

Akbar: Always studying, always working. You spend your
waking hours making others happy. Yet you get nothing
in return.

Shaheen: Indeed I am rewarded. My family are all around
me, running the business, while I get what I have always
wanted – peace to study and read my books.

Akbar: Tell me one thing that you want, one thing I can buy
for you in return for all your kindness to us.

Shaheen (*still engrossed in her book*): Yes.

Akbar: Shaheen, best daughter of all, take time to utter one word, so that I can search the world for whatever rare object your heart desires.

Shaheen (*turning a page*): *Sabar!*

Akbar (*puzzled*): *Sabar?*

Shaheen (*not really listening*): Please, Father – *sabar!*

Akbar: *Sabar* it shall be, whatever it is. Whatever a "*sabar*" is, you shall have it.

> *Exit Akbar. Shaheen gets up slowly, still reading, and walks into the house. The First Storyteller enters.*

First Storyteller: Do you remember what "*Sabar*" means? In the dialect of the country where Shaheen has built her house, it means "Be patient". But Akbar thought it was some special thing Shaheen wanted. So Ahmed, his faithful servant, goes all over the world looking for the best "*Sabar*" he could find. This was not an easy task – for there was no such thing as a "*Sabar*". You want to know what happens? Well – *sabar!* Be patient!

> *Exit Storyteller. Enter Ahmed, walking wearily.*

Ahmed: I have searched for weeks looking for a *sabar* – without success.

> *Enter four townspeople.*

Ahmed: Tell me, my friends, where can I buy a *sabar*?

All laugh.

First man: This is surely a joke!

Ahmed: If it's a joke, I've travelled miles for nothing.

Second man: Whoever heard of anyone buying a *sabar*?

They all laugh.

Enter Prince Omar, with two attendants and the Court Magician. The townspeople bow.

Prince: What's going on? Leave the poor man alone. Be off with you.

Townspeople go off.

Prince: Now, my man. Tell me what you are looking for.

Prince Omar, Ahmed and the Court Magician talk.

First Storyteller: So Ahmed tells the Prince about Akbar wishing to reward his good daughter Shaheen with a "*sabar*". The Prince resolves to meet this unusual girl who, like him, is interested in herbs and healing.

Prince: You are a faithful servant, Ahmed. I'm sure my Court Magician has the *sabar* you have been seeking.

Ahmed: Mighty prince, I thank you.

The Court Magician steps forward.

Court Magician: I call upon the magic power,
Bring me a *sabar* this very hour.
Abracadabra! Abracadee!
May the *sabar* be all that we want it to be!

The lights dim. The Court Magician turns upstage. There is a sound of a cymbal – and he turns to the Prince with a small, sparkling box in his hands.

Ahmed: That is a *sabar*?

Court Magician: Indeed it is. This box contains a fan. Your lady Shaheen must open it when she is quite alone – and then see what she shall see.

Ahmed (*wonderingly*): That is a *sabar*?

Court Magician: More or less.

The Court Magician gives Ahmed the box.

Ahmed: Thank you, thank you. I will return at once to my master.

Ahmed bows, and hurries off.

Prince: And now, my friend – tell me what will happen when Shaheen uses the fan.

Court Magician: By my powerful magic, you will be immediately transported to her side. When she sees you, she will see her "*sabar*" complete.

Prince: As "*sabar*" means "be patient", that is indeed myself. For I have been patient many years, waiting to find a girl like Shaheen. If she is as they say, I think I will make her my princess.

Act 2, Scene 3

(Outside Shaheen's house. A small table is by the door. Akbar is pacing up and down impatiently. Ahmed rushes in, very excited.)

Akbar: Ahmed, at last you're back.

Ahmed: I got here as fast as I could!

Akbar: Well, have you got the *sabar?*

Ahmed: Have I got it!

Akbar: Well, have you?

Ahmed: Don't you know Ahmed the brave, Ahmed the willing, Ahmed the strong can get anything in the world?

Akbar: Not really. And not often.

Ahmed (*crestfallen*):   Well, this time I did, but if you don't want to hear about it . . .

Akbar: Forgive me, Ahmed. Please let me see it.

Ahmed hands him the box.

Akbar (*a bit disappointed*):   Is this it? It looks a bit ordinary. (*He starts to open it.*)

Ahmed: Don't open it! The Prince got this from the Court Magician. Only Shaheen may open it.

Akbar: A Prince and a Magician! And they know about our
   Shaheen?

Ahmed: Yes, and she must be alone when she opens it – or
   the magic of the *sabar* will not work.

Akbar: I will send Shaheen at once.

*Exit Akbar. Ahmed places the box on the table, bows to it,
and goes. Soft music is heard. The lights dim, except for a
pool of light on the little table. Shaheen enters.*

Shaheen: What can it be,
   the mysterious *sabar*,
   The gift my father had
      brought from afar?
   "*Sabar*" means be patient,
      or so it would seem,
   Could this be the promise
      of the magic dream?

*She opens the box, and takes
out a beautiful sparkling fan.*

Shaheen: How lovely! I've made
   so many fans – but this
   one is for me!

*She fans herself in a sweeping dance-like
fashion. Prince Omar appears.*

Prince: So you are Shaheen.

Shaheen: Who are you?

Prince: I am Prince Omar Sabar. I have always wanted to find someone like you.

Shaheen: Like me? You don't know anything about me.

Prince: I know you are good, I see you are fair, and I hear that you spend your time seeking remedies.

Shaheen: You're interested in herbs and healing?

Prince: They are my constant study. If you marry me, we could work together to find cures for all the troubles of the world.

Shaheen: I don't think I would make a very good princess.

Prince: I am a prince – who wants to be a doctor.

Shaheen: I would marry a doctor, if I could work as a doctor too.

Prince: Then it is settled.

Enter Akbar and Razia.

Shaheen: Father, Mother, may I present Prince Omar Sabar.

Akbar (*aside to audience*):   This is a *sabar*! Well!

Prince: Sir, I would like to marry your daughter Shaheen.

Akbar: But of course, my dear Prince!

Razia: What has Shaheen to say? Are you happy, my daughter?

Shaheen: Very happy, Mother.

Akbar: Then we are happy too. Where are your sisters? All the family must rejoice together.

Razia (*calling*): Girls, come at once.

Enter Shaheen's sisters. They bow to Prince Omar in awe.

Razia: Prince Omar, may I present Shaheen's sisters – Sophia, Zara, Rayesa, Zarreen, Mahreen and Nadia.

The six sisters bow to Prince Omar.

Prince (*to Akbar and Razia*): What a charming family you have!

Razia: Happy news, my daughters. Prince Omar and Shaheen are to be married.

Sophia: How lovely!

Zara: Congratulations.

Rayesa: Imagine! A real prince!

Zarreen: And so handsome!

Mahreen: And you'll be a princess, Shaheen.

Nadia, the youngest, bursts into tears.

Nadia: I want to be a princess too!

Razia: Stop that at once, Nadia.

Shaheen: But I'm not going to be a princess!

All (*except Prince Omar*): What?

Shaheen: No. Omar and I are going to be doctors.

Akbar: But what about your country? Who will rule over it?

Prince: I shall hand the throne to my brother, Prince Anjum, who is next in line. He will be helped by our younger brothers Prince Faraz, Prince Zaki, Prince Haroun, Prince Nabil and Prince Saad.

Shaheen's sisters have been counting the princes silently, as Omar names them.

Prince: And none of them, as it happens, is married.

Shaheen's sisters brighten up considerably.

Akbar: Perhaps your brothers will attend the wedding feast.

Prince: Better than that. Perhaps I should introduce them now.

All (*astonished*): Now?

Prince: What is the point of having a Court Magician if you don't employ him? We will send a message.

Enter Mr and Mrs Bird.

Mr Bird: Can we perhaps see what we can do?

Prince: I need a messenger to go to the Court Magician in my palace far over the seas?

Akbar: I know – Ahmed!

All call loudly for Ahmed.

Enter Ahmed. The Prince, who has been writing, gives him a scroll.

Prince: Ahmed, I want you to fly across the sea for me. Give this letter to my Court Magician.

Ahmed: Fly? Me? Fly? Oh no!

The Birds swoop off, Ahmed between them, still protesting. Everyone applauds. There is a short silence.

Sophia: What happens now?

Prince: Ahmed will give the magician my message, and my brothers will be here in a trice.

Nadia: How long is a trice?

Prince: As long as it takes to count up to ten. All count together! Even you! (*This last comment to the audience.*)

All: One – two – three – four – five – six – seven – eight – nine – ten.

There is a clash of cymbals and the six princes, splendidly attired, enter. Each goes straight to one of Shaheen's sisters. Ahmed enters, exhausted. The Birds follow.

Ahmed: Everyone has someone – except me.

Enter Sabeen.

Sabeen: Isn't anyone coming to help me sell these fans?

All laugh. She links arms with Ahmed.

Prince: The message is "*Sabar*". If patient you are,
All things will come true with happiness for you.

(THE END.)

Teacher's Notes

This play is a dramatised version of various elements drawn from folk tales of the Indian sub-continent. It is set in the India of long ago, in the kind of landscape represented in the pictures in illustrated manuscripts from India that may be found in art galleries and museums or reproduced in books.

The story of Shaheen, whose forthright and honest opinions enrage her father, who is foolish enough to prefer the flattery of her vain sisters, is similar to many stories from other parts of the world. Often it is the youngest brother or sister who is at first rejected, then goes on to win through to a position of power, wealth and happiness. This theme is present in Cinderella, in Beauty and the Beast, and many others. The youthful hero or heroine often finds help from supernatural sources or from the world of nature, just as Shaheen meets kindness and friendship from the Birds and the Sheltering Tree.

The plot moves through several episodes where there are conflicts and confrontations between good and evil; justice is finally seen to be done, and repentance and reconciliation lead to a satisfactory happy ending for everyone. The play makes a good starting point for an integrated arts programme. There is ample opportunity for dance drama as well as speaking parts. The set, costumes and stage properties can be discussed and researched, and folios of designs may be produced in group work.

Costume

The costumes for the main characters may be inspired by looking at books of traditional Indian dress, pictures of theatrical designs, and illustrations from books of folk tales. Remember imaginative and colourful costume is more important than detailed accuracy.

Mr and Mrs Bird and the peacocks could be dressed in tunics or leotards and tights in appropriate matching colours. The peacocks' tails could be represented simply by a long piece of material hung from the waist, painted to simulate the blue-green feathers. The peacock feathers that are dropped on the ground should be made out of paper or cloth, and held behind the back, to be scattered at the required moment.

The Birds' costumes might be given some humorous detail, such as a waistcoat and bow tie for Mr Bird, and a hat and perhaps shoes with a little heel for his wife. Their wings can be created from soft, floating material, fastening, rather like a cape, at the throat, and attached with tapes to the wrist. Hoods with beaks like visors over the eyes would complete the picture.